THE LITTLE BOOK OF HEROES

www.littlebookofheroes.co.uk

This book is published by Grosvenor House Publishing Ltd
Crossweys, 28-30 High Street, Guildford, Surrey, GU1 3HY.
www.grosvenorhousepublishing.co.uk

A CIP record for this book
is available from the British Library

ISBN 978-1-907652-16-5

Dear Reader,

You may be unaware that all around the world there are schools dedicated solely to the education of services family's children. Unlike schools in the UK, many of the children and young people who start the school year are never the same as the ones who finish it! This is because the majority of our children and young people will move schools every two to three years as the parent is posted to their next assignment. This is something that most children do not experience in the UK, the majority attending one primary school and then transferring to one senior school.

When we approached the schools at the beginning of the year and invited them to join in with this project, the only instruction was that the children and young people wrote about 'Their Heroes'. As you would expect, many of the older students wrote about family members who are either serving on the frontline or who have in the past served their country and risked their lives. Our younger children had a slightly different take on the whole 'hero' theme. As with most children of Primary age they focused on superheroes or people who played a key role in their life (grandmothers, grandfathers, brothers sisters etc).

These younger children also focused more on the funny and the humorous rather than the sad and emotional – some of the contributions are from 5 and 6 year olds and whilst they know that Mummy or Daddy go away they often don't really fully understand the seriousness of what their parent is doing.

The teaching staff and especially the children have had a wonderful time putting The Little Book of Heroes together and hope that not only will it raise a lot of money for Help for Heroes but may also help the morale of all of the services personnel bravely fighting for their country.

I would personally like to thank Kim, Jason and Tamsin from Grosvenor House Publishing Ltd. who made this all possible.

On behalf of everyone involved in the creation of this book, we would all like to thank you for making this very special purchase.

Lynda Fisher

Lynda Fisher,
Chief Executive Service
Children's Education

SERVICES CHILDREN'S EDUCATION

Service Children's Education (SCE) is responsible for the provision of education for the children of Her Majesty's Armed Forces and other members of the Ministry of Defence (MoD) and sponsored organisations stationed overseas.

The schools are situated in nine countries: Belgium, Belize, Brunei, Cyprus, Falkland Islands, Germany, Gibraltar, Italy and the Netherlands; and together are attended by more than 10,000 children (including more than 1,400 children in the FS1 settings).

As an Agency of the Ministry of Defence, SCE follows the National Curriculum for England – from Foundation Stage through to sixth form. SCE seeks to provide a first class system of schools and educational support services and aims to provide an effective and efficient education service, from Foundation Stage through to sixth form, and to enable children to benefit from their residence abroad.

CHILDREN 'R' HEROES

by Mrs Maria McConnell, Teacher at John Buchan School

I know 300 heroes all young and very strong.

Their daddies go to war and sometimes mummies too

Many days and many nights they wait for their return,
in between, a phone call a letter even a face on a photo.
But these boys and girls remain strong for the families
left at home.

A calendar sits alone, each day the children mark
off how many days till Dad or Mum is home.

We keep the children safe and happy not letting them
forget, the reason they are here is because mum or
dad is their Hero.

Army life for us is great, we're happy, safe and thankful
that it won't be long before we are all together again.

We think of families who are not so lucky and
pray that's never us.

I see these children every day, and wouldn't
have it any other way.

PARTICIPATING SCHOOLS

ANDREW HUMPHREY SCHOOL	WILDENRATH	GERMANY
AYIOS NIKOLAOS SCHOOL	AYIOS NIKOLAOS	CYPRUS
BISHOPSPARK SCHOOL	PADERBORN	GERMANY
BLANKENHAGEN SCHOOL	GUTERSLOH	GERMANY
BRUGGEN SCHOOL	ELMPT	GERMANY
DHEKELIA SCHOOL	DHEKELIA	CYPRUS
EPISKOPI SCHOOL	EPISKOPI	CYPRUS
GLOUCESTER SCHOOL	HOHNE	GERMANY
HAIG SCHOOL	GUTERSLOH	GERMANY
HORNBILL SCHOOL	SELATAN SERIA	BRUNEI
JOHN BUCHAN SCHOOL	HOHNE	GERMANY
KING'S SCHOOL	GUTERSLOH	GERMANY
ROBERT BROWNING SCHOOL	SENNELAGER	GERMANY
SHAPE INTERNATIONAL SCHOOL (BRITISH SECTION)	MONS	BELGIUM
SIR JOHN MOGG SCHOOL	DETMOLD	GERMANY
SLIM SCHOOL	HOHNE	GERMANY
ST ANDREW'S SCHOOL	RHEINDAHLEN	GERMANY
TOWER SCHOOL	DULMEN	GERMANY
WINDSOR SCHOOL	RHEINDAHLEN	GERMANY
WILLIAM WORDSWORTH SCHOOL	SENNELAGER	GERMANY

Contents

OUR MILITARY HEROES

OUR FAMILY HEROES

OUR OTHER HEROES

Our Military Heroes

Help for Heroes Poem

Thomas Fox, Age 11
John Buchan School

Heroes are born not made
Every soldier is humble not vain
Live and let live on operations today
Paraded through the street union flag in tow

Fallen heroes are welcomed home
Orders are given
Rifles are prepared and cleaned

Heroes advance forward
Enemy within sight
Rounds are fired
Operation ends
Every man helps
Supporters are heroes

My dad is a hero.

Unseen Hero

Talei Sigatolu, Age 12
Windsor School

Where was my dad on my first birthday?
Where was my dad when I turned ill and grey?
Where was my dad when I needed him most?
Where was my dad when we walked to the coast?

He's been in Afghanistan that's where he's been
Years have gone by and now I'm a teen
He never came back from Afghanistan
He joined the army and now he's a man

My dad's an unseen hero that is mine
Brave, heroic and funny at times
Now we can't see that smile on his face
We pray to him now with all our grace.

The End

Kate Aston, Age 11
John Buchan School

The door flew open
A man stood there
With a steely expression
And mouse grey hair
Over his shoulder a jeep I saw
With men in the back
Their hearts so sore
I heard a door slam, then bang and splash
Bangs and boxes came down with a crash
My dad kissed me goodbye
Then climbed into the jeep
And off he went to the dangerous deep.

That night was so awkward
Nobody spoke
We ate dinner in mourn for those poor blokes.

Letter after letter was received and sent
Dripping with love in the entire content
The next letter that came was not from Dad
But from the Commander warning the news was bad.
A new operation had been held
In a brand new corner of this unknown world
There had been landmines everywhere
Most of them marked
And when the news came
My world went dark.

My Hero

Mollie Darke, Age 12
King's School

There's a hero I know,
Strong, broad but not too tall
Lives he saves month after month
Then when he's back
He's the greatest dad I know!

Brave and filled with courage
Such a fearless person
But when he's out there fighting for other people
I'm sure in his head
He's feeling out of place, out of heart and out
of mind!

His courage shines bright
Through the clouds in the summer skies
He loves us more than anyone could love
And we're always in his heart
And he will always be in mine

There's a hero that I know
Caring with a great sense of humour
So loving so kind and joyful;
He is the greatest hero I will ever know!

Hero

Amy Shepherd, Age 11
Shape International School (British Section)

The battle seems over,
Shouts and cries quieten,
As distant guns echo,
Smoke covers the land in grey clouds.

Bodies lie silent and still,
Side by side they wait,
For angels to call them,
The sour smell of sweat fills the air.

Buildings and roads all destroyed,
Silently watching the world go by.
Smashed and broken in a pile of dust.

In the evening through a cloud of smoke walk the
survivors.
The only survivors,
All the people who fought today are heroes.

REMEMBER THEM!

Arthur Lincoln Hornsby

Rhiannon Clarke, Age 10
John Buchan School

When you step foot on the battlefield, you hear the
guns roar.
You want to turn back but you just can't.
You want to wake up out of the nightmare.
But you can't

You have to fight for your life and other people,
When you feel the pain, you just cannot carry on....
But you must.

You carry on for your life and others' lives.
Your family is scared and so are your friends.

Arthur was brave and helped save peoples' lives.
He felt the pain too and fell to the ground.
The people rushed to save him, but it was just
too late.

We pray for all the soldiers.

Rest In Peace.

My Hero

Eva Rea, Age 10
Shape International School (British Section)

Heroes are life savers who risk their own lives for others.
They are brave and courageous and always there to help you when in need or pain.
Heroes do not give up, they persevere and never seek glory or gain.

My hero is a pilot who flies to the rescue of injured soldiers.
He goes to work, but that can often mean war.
He travels to lots of countries but not all are peaceful.
He flies for our freedom, country and Queen, to protect his family, friends and innocent people.

My hero,

This pilot

My dad!

Army Life, Home Life

Lukas Phillips, Age 9
St Andrew's School

Tanks, guns and murder,
Peace and harmony.
Loud screams of agony.
Safety, warmth - that's the life for me.
Death, blood, heart and body slowing.
My heart is broken by the coffins being towed.

Wootton Bassett

Travis Turnbull, Age 14
Gloucester School

Wootton Bassett what a village
What a place
Every time a fighting hero falls
The people of Wootton Bassett are there to call.

When the fallen hero is flying home
The soldier with a bullet in his dome
Wootton Bassett freeze to see him arrive
The family there to say their goodbyes.

Wootton Bassett what a village
What a place
Every time a fighting hero falls
The people of Wootton Bassett are there to call.

So very young at only eighteen
Fighting for his country and his queen
The enemy have little fear
He let his guard down when danger was near

Wootton Bassett what a village
What a place
Every time a fighting hero falls
The people of Wootton Bassett are there to call.

My Dad is Leaving

Carys Larwood, Age 8
St Andrew's School

My dad is leaving.
He left today.
Crunching down the gravel
Into the battered car,
Waving goodbye
Wiping away the tear
That is rolling down his cheek.
I turn round, can't bear to see him go.

My dad is leaving.
He left today.
I wonder,
When will I see him again?
I want my dad.

My dad has left.
I didn't want him to go.
The next time I'll see him
Is when it starts to snow.

Heroes

Kate Collins, Age 13
Windsor School

They brave their lives on the front line,
Taking bullet wounds for their country,
They come home like everything is fine,
Appreciated by their society,
They brave the worst conditions for us,
Living in fear day and night,
Getting on with their job; making no fuss,
Knowing what they are doing is right,
When they return home after months of war,
The sounds of battle disturb their dreams,
After the battle they feel alone and sore,
They are scarred for life; that is how it seems,
They will return home, some scared some not,
And for that we thank them a lot.

Each Letter

Charlene O'Dwyer, Age 12
Windsor School

One letter, one word,
Each tear means more
Everyday a new letter,
But no voice

For the first time
My dad left for Afghan
But all I want
Is his voice and time

Every letter sealed
With a sticker and a kiss,
Why is he there?
Why my dad?

R and R is worth waiting:
Dad's love will be home
With every tear I hear his voice,
Again and again.

My Dad the Hero

Karl Northey, Age 11
Windsor School

I pray to God
And hope he doesn't go away
But he comes back the next day
And says
"I have to go to Afghan"
I burst into tears
And so did mum

I was dreaming that night about
Bombs, guns and everything else
But I can't stop him – he has to go!

I am waiting month after month
I am still in touch with dad with email

I'm watching the news
And hearing roadside bombs have gone off

It is time for him to come back
Everyone shouts and I run up to him
And say;

WELCOME BACK DAD!

Unsung Heroes

Liam Davidson, Age 13
Windsor School

I awoke
I stared across the blood soaked trench
The stench of death was here once more
The silence was deafening
For all to hear
The everlasting taste of fear
It was the night before the infinite woe
The day was nigh
The men would go
I can see them running
Through my mind
"Attach bayonets"!
"We can do it blind"!
Over the top I hear them cry
The whistles blow
The men would die.

Mummy, my Hero

Megan MacGregor, Age 12
Windsor School

We miss him so much when he goes away,
No matter what happens, my mummy will say
"Don't worry my darling all will be fine
No fear, my dear, you will always be mine."

I squirm in my bed, no sleeping tonight
Why was he chosen to leave us and fight?
But mummy gets ill now what do I do?
I make her some soup and a cup of tea too.

I hope and I dream that she'll be alright,
I'm praying to God with all of my might
I walk in her room and hand her the mug
What she needs now is a humungous hug
Don't worry my darling, all will be fine
No fear, my dear, you will always be mine.

My Dad is my Hero

Children of 3C and 4G, Ages 7-9
William Wordsworth School

When my Daddy is away.........

I hate not spending time with him
I miss everything about him
I miss rough and tumbling in the garden
I miss him making me laugh
I miss stories and cuddles before bedtime
I miss him tickling me
I miss him because he is not here for me
I am scared that he might get hurt.

When my Daddy is at home............

I love it because he says he will love me forever
I love it because he is silly with us so we don't get
  into trouble!
I love it because he is strong like a bear and carries
  me up to bed when I am too tired to walk
I love it because he makes us laugh when he is late
  for work and running around like a headless chicken

My Daddy is a soldier and he is a hero because..............

Even when he's missing me he works hard
He protects other people even when he does not
  always know them

He has to spend so much time away from us and he never complains
He is always really brave even if something is very scary

Even when he is not with me I know that he loves me and I am very proud of him.

There He Goes

Joseph Watts, Age 11
Windsor School

There he goes again
How would I know
Whether he'll come home?
No time to say goodbye
He's gone before you can ask why
There he goes
On his plane
To another country again
Why does he go to all these countries
Just to stare in the face of death
He goes to serve his country
That's what a hero would do
Brave, daring and ever so caring
That's what my dad is
A hero that hasn't even been noticed.

Everything goes Wrong when my Hero is Away

Abbie Fox, Age 12
Windsor School

Everything goes wrong when my hero is away!
Ollie, the dog, goes berserk every day,
Ella and Joseph don't sleep at night
When he comes back I see the light
Thinking of him all the time
Taking him away, I think is a crime

I stopped and thought how it could be
If it was just him and me
Hugging and questions at what it's like
Him feeling like a brand new bike

He being away is really hard
So I send him a great big card

My biggest hero is my dad
When he's away I feel really sad.

My Dad the Soldier

Sophie Blackmore, Age 12
Windsor School

Why to me? Why to me?
It's really hard to see
Why is it MY dad has to go?
And nothing can change it, not even no
Seeing him leave, bags fully packed
I know he might not come back,
Horrible thought but it's a fact
Seeing him leave, in his desert-coloured coat
Keeping in touch is done by a note
Messages are special and phone calls are long
Afghanistan is not a dance and a song
Internet to keep in touch
He needs to know that I miss him so much
Six months is a long time to wait
When my dad is in a country full of hate
But to see them come back, the whole squadron there
I thank the Lord for answering my prayer
So now I have him at home at last
But soon the future will repeat the past
My dad is a soldier this life's all I know
He is MY dad, my biggest hero.

Do You Realise?

Chelsea Szczypior, Age 13
Windsor School

It's not just superman
Who can save you from the dark
It's not just spiderman
Who helps you when you're stuck
Cos just to let you know
A soldier does it too

Do you know how brave they are
Do your really care
When they go away
Their families shake with fear
They do it for you
They do it for me

He puts his life on the line
Going to places in Afghanistan
He manages to smile
When he comes through the door
Dad you're back we shout with glee
My brothers and sisters we're all happy

He's home
He did his job
He is a hero
He is my dad
And I thank you for that.

Hero

Cameron Lone, Age 11
Tower School

A war is terrible it makes me cry
A soldier is a hero and heroes die
We remember those whose loved ones are gone
They're brave and tough strong and bold
But none of us really know what it's like to go
And fight wars and save lives
To ponder thoughts of a lost friend
It makes me sadden deep inside
My heart will mend in time.

Heroes

Shannon Richardson, Age 12
King's School

Our heroes are many
Our heroes are as one
Our heroes proudly hold a gun
Our heroes sacrifice
But they don't surrender

Our heroes are together
Now and forever
Our heroes are clever, witty too
Our heroes kill
But don't senselessly slay

Our heroes are away
But not to stay
They too count down the days
Most come back secure
But the others are in our thoughts for sure.

Soldier's Sonnet

Lorna Dean, Age 14
Windsor School

Soldiers are heroes they fight for us all,
Away from their homes away from their lives,
They may be far away but still can call,
Back home to their friends, back home to their wives,
Soldiers are volunteers for death's grey land
Soldiers are sworn to action; they must win,
The heat of the desert; ready they stand,
Soldiers are daring when the guns begin,
Soldiers stand tall they do their jobs with pride,
They fight for others in a foreign land,
Coming home to those who when they left cried,
To those in need, hold out a friendly hand,
Heroes step forward it's life or the grave
One life's been given, for more to be saved.

A Soldier's Daughter

Zoe Lewin, Age 13
Gloucester School

Often away, no time to play; the Army takes its dues.
I sit upon my cosy bed waiting for good news.
It's been six months; his work's near done.
His return's not long to make us one.

He sits upon his makeshift bed waiting for his orders,
He has been told he will have to go across the distant
borders.
He and his soldiers have a brotherly bond, never to
be broken,
Sacrifice, a selfless gift, signifies the token.

I spend my days on what to do,
But most of the time it's "Dad I miss you".
At home I'm no help to my mum at all,
Without my dad I feel so small.

He's out in Afghanistan 24/7
I think to myself it's nothing like heaven.
I want him home with me today,
We can cuddle and laugh, and shout and play.

He's fighting the Taliban day and night.
I ask myself "is this our fight?"
Another six months, another tour
A far away land, with another war.

My friends at school are happy and loud,
They say to me that I should be proud.
It won't be long till my dad is out,
And that's the time I should be happy and shout.

My mum has said dad's coming today,
I'm happy that we can finally play,
He's standing there at the door, like he had done before,
Dad has told us he won't have to go to Afghanistan any more.

My Daddy's Going Away

Joe Ryan, Age 9
St Andrew's School

My daddy's going away,
Me and my sister want him to stay.
My best friend William said, "it'll be alright".
My mum says "he leaves tomorrow night".

My Daddy waved, "Goodbye"
He went to war with his head held high

He promised, "I'll phone when I get there".

My Daddy's gone far away
And we all wanted him to stay!!!!

My Mum, My Hero

Alisha Harrington, Age 11
Windsor School

Why my mum?
Why does she have to go?
She's serving this country
Yes, I know.

The glistening in her eyes
The tears that she cries
I miss her so much
I hope we stay in touch

She makes me smile
After not seeing her for a while.
She's travelled so far
She's such a star

She's saving lives
She deserves a prize:
My Mum, my hero.

The Soldiers

Keeley-Ann Hudspeth, Age 9
John Buchan School

They fight and fire,
They are my desire,
They conquer and they battle,
Even when the world rattles,
They help people,
When they don't know what to do,
They're honest and thoughtful,
We should be grateful.
The whole world should be grateful,
If one of them is your Dad,
You'll know what I'm talking about,
If one of them is your Dad,
He will make you proud,
When he comes back and you see him in the crowd,
And that is what I'm talking about,
They earn medals because of their work,
And they pin them on their uniforms.
Knowing they have your support.

Our Heroes

Rebecca Barrett, Age 10
John Buchan School

I miss my Dad.
I need him, more than a balloon needs air,
But everyone should know that they haven't gone
for war
They have gone to help people's lives get better.
I want him home because:
Dinner isn't the same any more without my Dad sitting
there.
My mum's now eating pears.
My sister and me are crying
You would think someone was dying
We heard on the news someone had attacked them
We were so scared
But they were so brave
He's our hero.

My Special Hero

Sam Dudley, Age 10
Shape International School (British Section)

My hero is my dad. He is a soldier in the Royal Signals, which is part of the Army. He has served in Iraq, Bosnia and Northern Ireland. My dad is my hero because he is kind and fun. I love it when my dad and I spend time together, especially when he takes me to see Nottingham Forest play, they are our favourite football team; they play at the city ground. I also love my dad's cooking; he makes a yummy Sunday roast. He makes me laugh when he tickles me.

I remember when my Dad left to go to Iraq; I was only four years old. I stood at the front door and cried and my mum gave me a cuddle. My dad was away for 6 months so I sent him pictures and blueys to cheer him up. He sent me a camel teddy which I still sleep with, even though my dog Buster chewed the nose off it!

My next adventure with my Dad will be in May when I fly to Australia, my Dad is joining the Australian Royal Signals and we are posted to Darwin. I feel a little bit scared, but I know my Dad will be there to look after me, my brother and my mum. I love my dad because he is always showing us new things and taking us to visit new places. My dad has taken us on lots of camping holidays around Europe, I liked Normandy, we visited the beaches and all the war graves and museums. My dad can't wait to show us around Australia.

The Brave Soldiers

William McNaught, Age 10
St Andrew's School

My Dad's in Afghan,
The Taliban near,
Soldiers thinking,
Why are we here?
But they've got a job to do,
Fighting for their country,
We're waiting at home.
Day and monthly,
Soldiers in Afghan,
Fighting a war,
Some survive,
Some fall to the floor,
They load their guns,
Rapidly,
When my Dad comes home,
We will live happily.

Hero

Connor Ramsay, Age 10
St Andrew's School

Months in Afghan.
Years in the army.

Hard as a bullet.
Everyday hero.
Risk anything for me.
Obviously my dad.

Our Hero

Cameron and Kieran McAdam, Ages 9 and 10
Tower School

Our dad is our hero
He's brave and bold
He's travelled the world
With stories to be told

He fights for our country
And fights for our Queen
Many a danger
He has seen

When he's away
We miss him so
When he has to leave
We don't want him to go

Dad we're very proud
Of all that you do
Keeping us saying

We love you!!

Hero

Lauren Harris, Age 13
Windsor School

Is it a bird, a plane?
No it's a hero
A hero is a saviour for all
The one who flies through the
Sky swooping down
Wearing a cape, leggings and pants
Is this a hero to you?
A hero to me is someone who
Fights in wars, wins battles
Just like our mums and dads.
They go out, fight for us,
Some don't even return,
But those who do
Are remembered as our heroes
A hero is someone who you look up to
Someone who deserves to be a hero
Our mums and dads deserve to be Heroes, but they
are not to some.
That is a hero to me.

He who was a Soldier

Sophie Sweetlove, Age 12
Windsor School

He who was determined
He who was so brave
He who was the strongest
For us, his life, he gave

He who was so fearless
His knowledge beyond compare
It's true he was courageous
But when he died, they didn't care

He who was so passionate
His confidence showed us all
How an honoured, loyal, fighter
At battle, to his death, could fall

He was unbelievably powerful
And with his generous manner
It's strange how defeat came his way
When in the skies, bullets did hammer

He who was a soldier
Who died so very young
But when the bullets kill some more
The battle's end will come.

You are my Hero

Gabby Slater, Age 14
Gloucester School

Off to war he will go, he will just leave and say,
"Look after your mum ok?"

Off he will go
He is my hero.

He leaves behind, his home, his children, his wife
As if it's the average thing, out there risking his life.

With his dignity he will go
He is my hero

He'll tackle the job, lion hearted courage so rare
And the constant inner strength that no measure on
earth could compare

I really hope he'll know.
He is my hero

He'll do what he can to keep his fallen proud;
I certainly know they are,
I just wish they could tell him aloud

Away he will go
He is my hero

He may not have fought in the trenches, Zulu or Boer,
But this soldier will keep up the fight until his battle
is over

To war he will go
He is my hero

He'll fight whoever it may be, they may well spit and taunt
But if only they could see, just what this man means to me

Fighting he will go,
He is my hero

He'll come back home, witty with his touch
He'll nick the T.V. remote and grin "missed me much?"

We do not speak about his time in war, the things he's seen and heard,
He will try to forget and one day they will bother him no more

When that time will one day come, I think you need to know
Dad, you will always be my hero, wherever you may go.

My Dad is my Hero

Chelsea Delve, Age 14
Gloucester School

My dad is my hero, he isn't just my dad he is a soldier in the British Army. He puts his neck on the line along with other male and female soldiers. When it comes to tours it hurts the wives and children but what we forget is it hurts them more. They're the ones that have to leave their families and they're the ones that see horrific sights. When soldiers are out in Afghanistan and Iraq they are still in danger whether they are sat in an office or on the front line. We owe a lot to these serving soldiers because if it wasn't for them the war would have spread into our country years ago. Everyone pays respect to those who have fallen in battle but we also need to pay respect to those who have survived.

My Dad, my Hero

Jack Welsh, Age 13
Gloucester School

On the frontlines every day,
Risks at every corner,
Vital decisions, flank to the left
Or suppress them with heavy fire?

Leading on from the battle at day,
Comes the nerving bombs at night
As the regiments wake
The alarm bells ring.

He secures communities
And saves the lives of innocents
To be loved is one thing
But to be a hero and a dad is another.

He's there, 6 months sleeping alone at night
And in return he has two weeks with us
Then before you know it
He's on the plane that he has dreaded.

The opposition do not realise
How much he means to me
If he is in sight, he'll see his loved ones no more
He is my dad, he is my hero.

My Hero

Johnny Bennett, Age 7
Episkopi School

Soldier that's my dad
Often goes away
Let's send him a letter
Dad misses us
I miss my dad
Ever so much
Really wish he didn't go away so much

My Hero

Hatty Wright-McCarthy, Age 11
Windsor School

He's brave,
He's daring,
He's been away,
I missed his silly sense of humour,
His everything,
His life

He went to Afghan,
Twice in fact,
But every time he came back.

Always gone,
Never here,
Camp to camp,
Never here.

My Dad,
My soldier,
My hero.

My Hero

Arun Rai, Age 10
Hornbill School

My hero is a soldier that is hard as a boulder
That is gallant as a knight and with a heart of a
mighty lion
Who is cunning as a fox, quick as lightning and strong
as Hercules.
A soldier who could stop a tank with one hand, a soldier
who has enemies that are scared to go through him.
A soldier who could save a whole country's life or the
whole wide world and a soldier who is loyal as a
friend,
Most of all, who is the bravest of the brave.

Soldier

Alan Walker, Age 13
Gloucester School

Saves the day,
Over the seas far from us.
Loving and caring.
Dead and not forgotten.
Inspiring everyone.
Energetic with the job.
Resilient at the job and not giving up.

My Dad

Akash Urung, Age 9
John Buchan School

Today
My dad went away
He won't be back till May
Is that okay

Sunday
My birthday
Still away
No way
Is that okay

It's May
Dad is in the doorway
He's here to stay
Hurray!!
That's okay

Tomorrow we're on holiday
Off on the motorway
That's okay
That's very much okay
Hurray!

Battlefield

Molly Whitehead, Age 12
John Buchan School

Some people go to a battle field,
And never leave again,
Some people go to a battle field,
And never find a friend

But for the family
What's left for them?
For the kids no Dad to hug
For the wives an empty space upon their double bed!

When they return
Tears are shed
Off they run to hug him
How grateful they are for his return and love beyond
the seas

Hero

Rory Clayton-Hurst, Age 11
Shape International School (British Section)

A man or woman who is strong and brave,
A person who cares more about others,
A loyal companion who will not leave your side,
A lionhearted individual who fights the enemy without anxiety.

A hero is born from courage and valour,
They persevere when all seems lost,
They don't forget you in the midst of battle,
They don't turn and flee like a coward.

They fight the enemy with anger,
For a comrade has fallen that day,
The enemy have cut down more men,
Furiously the hero attacks, protecting his comrades.

As he fights he is hit by a bullet,
Yet he still battles on like a lion,
The hero is lagging now but still struggles on,
Warns the men to pull back to camp.

The hero refuses to retreat with his men,
When suddenly a bullet claims him,
The men don't realise their hero has fallen
Dead but not forgotten.

My Dad the Hero

Adam Lewis, Age 10
Sir John Mogg School

My dad is not a soldier going to fight the Taliban, he is an army teacher. He teaches soldiers to operate guns and sometimes goes to Hohne, in Germany, to teach. My dad takes me fishing. Once I caught a fish, it weighed 26 pounds I caught it over night. Most of the carp fish are out at night. It was the biggest carp fish caught in my family. We have lots of fun at Christmas.

When I was little, my dad went away. He was not here for Christmas, it was sad having one parent for Christmas, but in the summer of 2006, my mum and my brother and me went to Cyprus to meet my dad. Even now, my dad is away sometimes. We still stay in contact over the phone. My dad loves me so much, he would fly to Pluto to get me if I had been abducted by a UFO!

My Dad is Going Away

Archie Campbell-Smith, Age 9
St Andrew's School

My dad is going away.
We will be sad.
He is off to plan an attack
On the very, very bad

My dad has gone away.
We miss him so much.
My mum says,
Sing happy songs in your head,
While you lie in your bed.

My dad is coming back,
We are so excited,
With his big back pack.

My dad is here now
We're very happy!!!!

Hero

Emily Jones, Age 11
Tower School

A hero makes peace
A hero saves lives
Fights for the country
And is willing to die

Brave as a knight
And as tough as a lion
Bold and courageous
Night and day

They march into battle
Without any fear
But you can see
Their secret tear.

My Hero – My Dad

Georgia McGhee, Age 12
Windsor School

Why did he have to leave me?
Why did he have to go away?
Tears trickle down his dull face
Bye was all he had to say
My mummy's heart was broken
Dad fighting for his life
Would he be alright and safe?
Hope that he'll stay alive
Always thinking of his jokes
That always made me smile
I'm distraught that he's not here
And he's gone for a while
Today my dad is back home
I'm thrilled and excited
Inspired and thankful
Proud and delighted
His bravery and courage
Has led me to believe
That my dad, the hero
Is able to achieve.

Man of the House

Luke Warrender & Kalum Harvey, Age 13
Gloucester School

When the hour arrives and Dad's off on tour,
The hallways all cluttered with kit and more.
We say our goodbyes; it's awkward and quick,
He's gone just as fast as your fingers click.

Our father's power is left in our hands,
Whilst he's away fighting in foreign lands.
Our mothers now call us man of the house,
We're the substitute for her missing spouse.

As he returns from the searing wasteland,
His clothes all covered in Afghan sand.
We wait at home for the doorbell to ring,
Then run to the door to welcome him in.

My Hero

Thomas Cummings, Age 8
Bishopspark School

I know someone who risks his life in war.
I know someone who makes me happy.
I know someone who is brave enough to climb a
mountain bare-footed.
I know someone who would walk 5000 miles on his own.
I know someone who will tuck me in bed at night,
My Dad

My Daddy

Georgia Young, Age 10
Andrew Humphrey School

He is very brave
He faces his fears
He goes away
To help other people
In Afghanistan and Iraq.

I am so proud
He keeps me smiling
So I can have a happy day
For he is so special
Because he SHINES
He inspires me in every single way
He wants the best for me
He gets us money for his hard work
My dad is responsible, independent, he nurtures me.

My dad wears his uniform proudly,
He is so courageous,
So independent,
Dependable
Because I can count on him
I love him with all my heart
He is my HERO.

Hero

Alanah Ferguson, Age 8
Ayios Nikolaos School

My heroes are the people
Who are in Afghanistan
Fighting in the war

You think how brave they are fighting in the war

How do we help when the heroes return?

Everyone can give love, hope and happiness

Recognise the sacrifice of the men

Owe them our respect and thanks again

My Hero is my Dad!!

Harry Searle, Age 8
Blankenhagen School

He works in the Army and is very important
The reason he is important is because he is in Afghanistan
He saves people and is very brave and full of courage
When I grow up I want to be just like my dad!!

Our Dad, our Hero!

Alex Grainger, Bradley Robinson &
Philip Douglas, Ages 6,6,5
Bruggen School

Our dads are amazing
They are wickedly cool and strong
They go to war and fix the tanks
We are sad when they are gone

My Dad drives a boat
My Dad is an Engineer
My Dad saves the day
Especially when he is here

I love how my Dad buys me things
And takes me up to bed
He is always around when I need him
He is forever in my head

So when he's away, I can have him in my heart.

Everyone is a Hero

Sophie Collinson & Hannah Storrie, Age 10
Episkopi School

A Hero thinks of others before they think of
themselves
A Hero will die to protect
A Hero can be any age, any colour
A Hero can be a man, woman or child
A Hero is courageous, loving and brave
A Hero will never complain
A Hero can be made in one act of compassion
Or years of tender loving care
Some Heroes are remembered, whilst
Others are left forgotten
Heroes are angels in disguise,
Saving precious innocent lives

A True Hero

Alexandra Cowlan, Age 9
Hornbill School

My hero is a candle lighting up the way
As majestic as a mountain lion
As fast as an asteroid
As protective as a guard dog
Trustworthy and cunning

A country protector
A hope projector
As persevering as life on Earth
They are magnificent beacons shining in the darkness

My hero is a soldier
As strong as a metamorphic boulder
They put out the flame of destruction
And light the candle of empathy
They serve their amazing country

They are as precious as golden dust
Only going to war to protect their country
An example to us all.

My Hero

Philip McHale, Age 9
Robert Browning School

He is always thoughtful and caring.
He is brave and bold like a lion protecting his cubs.
He is as clever as a dog learning his tricks.
He never picks on others but stands up for them!
He is very kind and does all the things he has to do!

That's my hero my DAD!!!

My Husband is a Soldier

Katherine Hunter, Age 13
Windsor School

My husband is a soldier
He's going out to war
He's away for many months
I hope the time's gonna soar

My husband is a soldier
We're waving our goodbyes
"When will dad be back, mummy?"
Tears then fill my eyes

My husband is a soldier
My children are so scared
They think he's left me with the kids
They think he's never cared

My husband is a soldier
I miss him terribly much
We write to him with blueys
So we can keep in touch

My husband is a soldier
Why did he have to go?
To risk his life, and save our own
He's forever my biggest HERO!

My Hero

Sophia Walsh, Age 10
Shape International School (British Section)

My hero is my dad
He is brave and courageous
He worked in Iraq and Afghanistan
He inspired me to do my part in the world
He inspired me to do all the things I do today
I love my dad with all my life
Through thin and thick and hard and easy
I will never leave him because I love him
My hero is my dad
He will always be it
He is like a brave lion
He is as kind as a panda

My Dad the Hero

Mark Witterick, Age 10
Sir John Mogg School

My dad is an excellent cook who is usually trying to teach me new and adventurous things or ways. Like when I was 8 he taught me how to make Scotch eggs and omelette. Also, he takes me out on treats all the time and I treat him by cooking or making him a cup of tea. Once he took me skiing at Winterburg and my sister fell over 27 times, and he used to take me with him when he went to hockey practice in the evening.

My dad has served in the army for 22 years he's getting out in 2012. He was 17 when he joined the army and has been to Canada twice, Oman, OP Herrick, Kosovo, Iraq and Afghanistan. He's an engineer armourer and a Sergeant, so he's good at making and fixing stuff. Also he's taken me to work with him a few times, and he used to take me with him when he went to hockey practice in the evening.

My dad is good at making stuff, he made me a board for my soldiers which I use often I helped decorate and make. He's fixed the telly and computer, also the car on more than one occasion. He was a bit of a naughty boy at school he once punched the teacher when he refused to let him go.

Hero

Scott Carson, Age 14
Windsor School

Is a hero someone we love?
Who fills our heart with glee
Or is a hero a superhero
With a super identity
Is a hero someone in war
Fighting to protect our rights
Or is a hero some freaky mutation
Unsung and kept out of sight
Is a hero a battlefield medic
Where duty endangers their life
Or is a hero a godly figure
Known for their sacrifice
Is a hero a caring friend
That always makes you feel good
Or is a hero someone who helps you
Just like everyone should

My Hero

Luca Corrado, Age 10
Sir John Mogg School

My hero is NOTHING without his gadgets,
Anything new is his, it's true!

He fixes my bed I help too
And his favourite colour is red and blue

He always puts gel in his hair,
Even when there's barely anything there!

My hero cooks the nicest meals.
And the best meatballs in the world,
Rarely does it go wrong and weird!

My hero, is fair, brave, loyal and honest.
He will refuse to give in
Even if it makes him scream and shout.

My hero goes to Afghanistan,
But does not fight the Taliban.
He builds things to help us win
This terrible war, which is full of sin.

My hero is the biking type,
He rides around on a KTM bike.

My hero makes me glad,
And I'm proud to call my hero "MY DAD!"

My Dad's not a Random Guy

Rosalind Favis, Age 9
St Andrew's School

My dad's not a random guy.
My dad's a special dad.
He goes away months at a time.
He has a special uniform.
Not always here for my birthday,
Not always here for Christmas.
Breaks his leg sometimes,
Breaks his arm sometimes.
So kind hearted,
So brave.
My dad's not a random guy.
My dad's a special dad.
My dad's a soldier.

Hero

Heather Baker, Age 13
Windsor School

What is a hero?
The men fighting
The doctors and nurses
The people protecting us
The teachers
To you they are heroes
But to me
A hero is the families
The ones at home
Keeping it all going
The ones who are helping the kids
The ones
Who are keeping the men going
The ones who will be there
When the men are back
The ones that have a shoulder to cry on
They,
To me are the heroes

My Heroes

Sian Nanton, Age 11
Sir John Mogg School

Mum's excellent at cooking,
She cooks the Sunday roast.
Mum's not the type of person
Who can't make toast.
She even was supportive,
When dad went to Iraq on the road.
Then baby brother was born,
And the dog had to be sold
THAT Mum is MY Mum and MY Mum is MY hero.

Dad's a mechanic and in the army,
He goes away but never worries
At least he comes back in one piece,
But when he goes again it's hard to release
Dad may be embarrassing,
When he tries to be cool,
With his t-shirt on backwards,
He says "it makes the ladies drool...."
But THAT Dad is MY Dad and MY Dad is MY hero.

So Mum may have cried when Dad had to leave
And Dad may have sworn when he hurt his knees....
But those parents are MY parents and My parents are MY heroes.

Soldier

Will Ross, Age 10
St Andrew's School

He waits in the trench,
Gun at the ready,
The command is given,
He climbs out the trench,
The enemy machine guns start to rattle,
But still he marches on,
His friends drop down dead or injured,
Know he is frightened,
He lies down in a dirty shell hole,
Praying to God to save his life,
He peers out the shell hole,
He pulls out his gun,
Takes aim and fires,
One of the enemy falls down dead,
But he's been spotted,
Quickly he crawls back to cover,
He looks in his pouch,
And pulls out a grenade,
And throws it in to an enemy trench,
BANG!
He sees his best friend,
Calling for help,
He crawls over to his friend,
His friend is injured,
He picks him up,
And runs as fast as he can back to the trench,
Risking his life,
He puts his friend down carefully,
His friend says You're my hero!

My Heroes

William Baxter, Age 10
Sir John Mogg School

The best thing about my dad is the fact that if he sees someone that's in trouble he will go and help. Like the time he was in the Falklands and he saw someone with live mines in the back of his car; you would think he would just run, but he stopped the man and helped him take the mines out of his boot. When he had finished he put the mines in a big pike and then threw a rock at them and the he had a 'bomb' fire.

My mum and dad have been married for 13 years and they gave birth to me in the year 2000. I have been raised as a single kid and I like to think that my dog is my brother. In my eyes everyone is a hero for who they are.

I would say that our mums have to do a lot of things like doing the shopping, washing and 9 times out of 10 they do the cooking, and when our dads are away they have to be 2 parents.

My Hero

James Briody, Age 11

Gloucester School

My hero is Corporal Andrew Briody. He was a soldier in both the 1st and 2nd World Wars. He is my hero because he was one of the thousands of soldiers who fought for our freedom today. He was also one of the thousands of soldiers who died for our freedom today.

I found out about my great uncle on the internet and in old diaries he kept during the wars. He said in one of his entries that he had saved his sergeant from being blown up by a grenade, he did it by bravely picking it up and throwing it back.

My great uncle is my hero because he was a brave man. He was always positive and he was resilient.

Dad

Charlie Jayne Young, Age 8

Andrew Humphrey School

Strong, healthy and kind
Sometimes off to Afghanistan
Cares for me with love

My Hero

Jodie McConnell, Age 8

Ayios Nikolaos School

My hero is my dad
He went to Afghanistan
People call him "Mad Dog"
And I don't really know why
And I love him so much

My hero is my dad
I felt very sad when he went away
I hoped he was going to be safe
And I was so happy when he came back!

Our Dad is our Hero

Teal Woodall, Age 6

Bruggen School

Our dad is a hero he's brave
And bold
He fixes cars and I'm sad when he is gone
I love my dad!

My Hero Daddy

Sydney Godwin, Age 6
Ayios Nikolaos School

My dad goes away but I always
Know he's safe
He protects all
He is a real life saver
He is the bravest of them all
He is so caring
He helps the ones who are injured
My dad is courageous
He loves to save people's lives
He's one of those people who are in the Forces
And I like him so much

My Dad

Daisy McMullan, Age 10
Andrew Humphrey School

He keeps me happy
Because he makes me giggle
My dad is very brave
Because he faces his fears
I am proud of my dad
Because he always works hard
And always keeps trying.
My dad does amazing things
Because he goes to Afghanistan and fights.
He wears his uniform proudly.
I love him more than anything in the world.
He is the most fun loving dad I know.

My Hero

Rhys Williams, Age 8
Ayios Nikolaos School

My hero went to war
He was in World War Two
He is a Welsh soldier
And he's really friendly
He's my Granddad
We walked to the old battlefield
We fed the ducks and chicks
He's always be a hero to me

Dad

Callum Wood, Age 9
Andrew Humphrey School

He is a brave man
He goes to Afghan a lot
He has shot a gun

Dad

Ciara Johnson, Age 9
Andrew Humphrey School

He is heroic
Courageous and so helpful
Never disappoints

Who's my Hero?

Danielle Rickman, Age 14
Gloucester School

A soldier is my hero,
Fighting for their nation,
They're not some lame old zeroes,
Counting down days for a vacation

In their camouflage costumes,
Out in sun and rain,
Fighting must resume,
Waiting to come home again.

Waiting to see children's faces,
And his lovely wife too,
For that warm embrace,
Children saying "Daddy I missed you"

Sometimes they're happy,
Sometimes they're sad,
Sometimes they're smiley,
Or feel really bad,

Do they deserve my respect?
Fighting every day,
Not knowing what to expect,
I'm behind them all the way.

Soldier

Keith Finlay, Age 13
Gloucester School

Soul saving.
Offering their lives.
Life saving daily.
Die for their country and for others.
Intelligent people.
Excellent at their jobs.
Ready to save lives.

Heroes

Sion Warren, Age 9
Slim School

Heroes running up and down trying to save a life

Exiting the building with a husband child and wife

Running down the street searching everywhere

Offering their lives for this, people stop and stare

Everyone imagines what it's like to be that bad

So it's just as well we have them there, heroes like my dad

Hero Poems – Y3 and 4 Haiku Poems

Dhekelia School

Courageous and brave
Unselfish, kind and helpful
Have no need for praise

Craig Jones, Age 9

Strong in heart and mind
Ordinary to look at
They know their brave deed

Amber Keen, Age 9

He is good and brave
Protecting my family
We love my daddy

Thomas Boginiso, Age 7

My hero
Bold and courageous
Someone who looks after you

Jake Butterfield, Age 7

Hero - strong and smart
Risking their lives for others
Putting them first

Connor Petterson, Age 9

Our Family Heroes

Our Heroes

Willow Class, Ages 5-7
Tower School

Our mum and dads are our heroes because they are....
Amazing and adorable
Brilliant and bubbly
Cuddly and cool
Dependable and on duty
Efficient and embarrassing
Funny and fantastic
Generous and great
Happy and helpful
Imaginative and ideal
Kind and kissable
Lovely and likeable
Magnificent and mighty
Nice and neat
Organised and outstanding
Perfect and protect me
Quirky and quality
Responsible and resourceful
Safe and strong
Talented and tough
Useful and up to date
Valuable and vital
Wonderful and works hard
Youthful and zany
Thank you mum and dad

Family Heroes

Adrian Clive, Age 12
Windsor School

Heroes don't need to have super powers
My heroes are the ones who love me forever
I wish we could always be together
They go on courses, sometimes weeks at a time
They seem to go on forever

My whole family are my heroes
When the other goes away
My parents still love me and
Get on with each day

But now I'm the one away from home
Being a boarder, not at home
"goodbye" I said to mum and dad
There are tears in my eyes and I'm feeling sad

I count the sleeps till I am home
I speak to them every day on the phone

I love my family so much
I can't wait till I see them again.

My Heroic Dad

Taylor Burgess, Age 10
John Buchan School

My dad was in Belize,
In year 2001,
He was building a school for the children,
Underneath the Caribbean sun.

He was on his way to work one day,
When a jeep in front of him crashed
It rolled over many times.
And was completely and utterly smashed.

Five people were seriously injured,
They were in a really bad way,
My dad gave them first aid and called an ambulance,
And really saved the day.

All five people survived that day,
In that tiny nation,
And my dad was on parade,
And was presented with a commendation.

My dad will always be my hero.

My Hero

Mollie Noone, Age 12
Gloucester School

My hero is my auntie
Because she is so kind
She made me so very loved
When I left my parents behind

At seven, I went to boarding school
At first I loved it there
But then we moved to Germany
Since then I didn't care

But my auntie kept me going
Telling me, "It's not that long!"
With all our wonderful times together
Her attitude kept me strong

Leaving my parents was the hardest
I didn't want to board the plane
I'd cry and cry until I was worn out
But my auntie kept me sane

At eleven, I decided
That I had to go back home,
After all, having a family
Is better than being alone

Although I miss my auntie,
I know that she will come
She'll call me at the weekend
And we'll have tons of fun!

My Hero

Olivia Warren-Nicholls, Age 8
Bishopspark School

My hero is trustworthy
As trustworthy as a mum cautiously watching out
for you
This makes me feel cheerful
My hero is caring
As caring as a wicked, wild cheetah
Anxiously staring out for her cubs.
This makes me feel safe
My hero is bold
As bold as a lion fiercely hunting for good
This makes me feel happy
My hero is friendly
As friendly as a mum caring for you
This makes me feel loved
My hero is my Grandpa!

Heroes

Alexander Malcolm, Age 8
Bruggen School

Mum

My hero is my mum
She really makes my day
She helps me with my homework
And that isn't much to say.

I love you Mum.

Dad

A hero is a person who's sticking up for others.
A hero is a person who's a kind and gentle man
A hero is a person who's fast and really quick

My Hero

Meghan Udale, Age 9
Bishopspark School

My hero is supportive
As supportive as a teacher guiding her pupils to successes.
This makes me feel secure and safe.

My hero is kindhearted,
As kind-hearted as a girl – gathering beautiful flowers for her mum.
This makes me feel cheerful

My hero is loving,
As loving as a deer gently caring for her baby fawns,
This makes me feel happy.

My hero is my

DAD!!!

My Hero

Selay Kesen, Age 5
Ayios Nikolaos School

My mum is a hero
Because she saved my cat
From the tree

My Dad the Beaver Leader

Charly Jones, Age 7
Episkopi School

My dad the beaver leader
Always makes it fun
Playing games and making friends
And letting us run, run, run

Rhino is what we call him
He is my biggest hero
I am so proud that he's my Dad
And without him I would be sad

I love my Dad x

My Hero Poem

Lucy Williams, Age 8
Bruggen School

My daddy is my hero
He is a boy
Filled with joy

My mummy is also my hero
She puts me in the bath
And we laugh and laugh

My daddy is cool, he rules.

My mummy is gentle
She loves lentil soup

My daddy is my hero
He is fearless.

My brother is my hero
He is heroic

I love my heroes.

My Hero

Epi Naiyaga, Age 11
Blankenhagen School

You are like a bulldozer strong and powerful
You are like a compass – you lead the way
Your hands are like pillows
Your voice is like a trumpet because you guide me on the road
You are my hero
You are my dad

My Hero

Blake Manuel Stamp, Age 9
Bishopspark School

She is not rich
She does not dance ....
But she shelters me when I'm sad
She is always my true friend
She is there when I need her
She hugs me to make me feel protected
She has a place in my heart
She is an honest person
She is my mum.

My Sister

Kobe Moor, Age 8
Bishopspark School

My hero is brave.
As brave as a speedy gorilla
Using his strong muscles leaping rope to rope
This makes me feel I would like to be her
My hero is irritating
As irritating as the tap dripping
Slowly into the dirty sink annoying me all night
This makes me feel pestered
My hero is pretty
As pretty as the moon glowing into her eyes
This makes me feel happy
My hero is my sister.

My Hero is my Mum and Dad

Leah Whatmough, Age 8
Ayios Nikolaos School

My heroes are my Mum and Dad
You've been here since my life began
Hardly ever getting cross, hardly ever getting mad
Every day we have so much fun
Really happy, never sad
Oh, my parents shine like the sun!

My Dad and Me

James Fraser, Age 10
Haig School

My dad loves me to the ends of the earth and back,
But what touches him even more is seeing
Me grow up
He's a soldier you know
A good one too,
He works a lot but sometimes he's home at half past two.
My dad and me love to play together
We play fight together
He's a great dad altogether
But best of all he gives up his spare time
Just to play with me.

My Hero

Emily Barclay, Age 9
Hornbill School

Noble as a lion
Mighty as a hurricane
Bold as a tiger,
My hero is a sign of hope in troubled times

My hero loves to help me out
My hero is always there for me

As sweet as the summer breeze
As kind as a spring lamb
Faster than a peregrine falcon
He buys me lovely presents
My hero loves all living creatures (except cats)

As loyal as an unbreakable bond

My hero is my Dad

FS 2 Hero Poems

Hornbill School

The children talked about people who were their heroes and why. They they came up with rhymes themselves and an adult helped to put the into sentences.

My sister likes to play
With me every day

Olivia Hunter, Age 5

My brothers and sisters live in the UK
When I'm there we like to play

Jennifer Chongbang, Age 5

My brother plays the guitar
I think he's a star

Edlyn Rai, Age 4

I have a brother called Jake
He likes to eat cheesecake

Tilly Dawes-Smith, Age 4

Batman has a bike
He rides in the night

Jonathon Hunter, Age 4

My sister has long hair
She likes puppies and teddy bears

Lisa Rai, Age 4

I like Ben Ten
He fights nasty men

Rachel Limbu, Age 5

Superman can fly
Across the sky

Pratap Hang Thebe, Age 5

My favourite power ranger is red
I play with the toy when I'm in bed

Kewal Maden Limbu, Age 5

My Hero

Ben Leach, Age 9
John Buchan School

My Hero is My Dad

Strong, fast, amazing
Stronger than me
Stronger than we
Brill, tall, fantastic
And he is alive.

My Heroes

Aidan & Neve Dempsey, Age 6
Ayios Nikolaos School

My hero is my nana
She helped me when I fell down the stairs
My friend is my hero.
He helped me when I forgot my Teddy at the NAAFI

My Hero

Elysha Overall, Age 9
Episkopi School

My hero is my mum because she always looks after me.
What could I do without her?
Who could make my tea?
She helps me clean my bedroom,
Even when it's a big mess!
She tucks me into bed every night,
My mum is really the best!!!

My Mum

Jasmine Rogers, Age 9
John Buchan School

Kind, elegant, lovely
As sweet as a cherry pie
She makes me feel light and fluffy
Nice, over-joyful, open-minded
She will always be here
Without her I would not be here
She helps me

Heroes

Cameron Sinclair, Age 7
Bruggen School

A hero is brave
A hero is strong
A hero sticks up for anyone

My dad is a hero
He helps me with my writing

My brother is a hero
He protects me when someone is mean

My mum is a hero
She helps me with my homework.

A hero is not afraid of bad people
A hero is not scared
A hero is the best

My Hero

Arim Rai, Age 10
Dhekelia School

My hero was born on earth
He is my dad.

Hero Poem

Phoebe Nowosielski, Age 7
Bruggen School

My mum is my hero.
She picks me up and gives me hugs.
My mum is my hero.
She makes me nice food.
My mum is my hero.

I love my mum.
My mum is my hero.
She helps me do the cleaning.
My mum is my hero.
She takes me on trips to Sea Life centre.
My mum is my hero.
She buys me nice things.

I love my mum.
My mum is my hero.
She looks after me when I am poorly.

I will always have time for you, Mum.

My Hero

Sophie Williams , Age 9
Bishopspark School

My hero is strong.
As strong as a super friendly muscle man lifting up enormous huge, heavy weights.
It makes me feel definitely brave and very strong.

My hero is fantastic.
As fantastic as a shooting star blasting off through the midnight sky splashing it's sparkles on top of me.
It makes me feel lucky to have him by my beautiful side.

My hero is skinny.
As skinny as a long, green string bean sizzling on a flat grey pan.
It makes me feel really joyful because my hero is skinny however, I love him for who he is.

My hero is my

Dad!!!

My Hero

Amber Wilkin, Age 10
Blankenhagen School

You are a bulldozer
You are strong and wise
You help me in a problem
You are funny like a monkey
You are as tall as a giraffe
You protect me like I am a gift
You are my hero
You are my dad.

My Hero

Isabelle Bailey, Age 6
Ayios Nikolaos School

My hero is my daddy because he saved my dog from losing her hair.

My Hero

Paddy Malloy, Age 8
Bishopspark School

I would swim with wild sharks,
I would climb the highest mountain,
I would go to the end of the world,
I would fight six mummy Boa Constrictor snakes,
I would go through every problem with him
He is my dad
My hero

Joe, my Hero

Amber Godwin, Age 6
Haig School

Joe is my big brother
Sometimes he is mean to me
Sometimes he is kind
He goes to boarding school

Once we were playing
In my Hanna Montana room
He saved me from falling over
And cracking open my head

Joe you are my hero

There's a Hero Out There

Abi Macintosh, Age 12
King's School

There's a hero out there
Her hugs soothe my pain
She brings sunshine
Into my heart
She guides me on the way

There's a hero out there
He protects me with his strong arms
I don't feel afraid once he's near
He brings a rainbow
After a storm

These heroes are great as they love me, so
They're the best everyone knows
My heroes are my mum and dad, because they
Care for me *everyway*

My Hero

Ben Davidson, Age 8
Bishopspark School

My hero is skilful.
As skilful as a gorilla carefully swinging tree to tree getting the tasty bananas.
This makes me feel inspired.

My hero is funny.
As funny as a silly clown making children giggle with laughter.
This makes me feel cheery and warm inside.

My hero is caring.
As caring as a lioness watching after her cubs.
This makes me feel safe.
My hero is my Dad.

My Hero

Rachel Walker, Age 9
Ayios Nikolaos School

My family
Yummy cakes

Huggable
Entertaining
Reg is my lovely granddad
On Skype we chat

My Mum's a Heroine

Ruth Johnson-Ferguson, Age 9
St Andrew's School

My mum's a heroine,
She takes me where I want,
At the weekends we go everywhere.
When I'm hurt she's always there.
My mum's a heroine,
I love her dearly,
Hopefully she loves me back.
My mum's a heroine,
She makes me laugh a lot.
I think this is her favourite saying,
Ruth, you've lost the plot!!

My Hero is my Dad

Elimae Kerslake, Age 7
Ayios Nikolaos School

My hero is my dad
Y? because I fell off my bike

He came to my rescue, he picked me up and cuddled me in his big arms.

Every time I need to be rescued he is always there for me

Remember your hero like I remember mine

Often the days will pass by before I hurt myself and cry, but always my daddy the hero is here for me.

Grandad in Fiji

Aaron Misimisi, Age 6
Haig School

When I go to Fiji
Grandad looks after me
He climbs up a tree to get an apple
To eat after my tea

Grandad takes me swimming
In the sea
He swims underneath
To save me from sharks

My Hero

Lauren Speight, Age 13
Windsor School

You are the one, who knows me best
When it's time to have fun and time to rest

Who's funny, courageous, brave and strong?
Who's intelligent and knows right from wrong?

You stand by me through thick and thin
Even when I did not win
And when I'm sad you gave me faith and hope
But you taught me how to cope

You are my cushion when I fall
You support me whenever I call
I am proud of what I am
Because I have the best mam.

Hero

Sarah Corps, Age 8
Ayios Nikolaos School

My hero is my dad
You know when he's around

He smiles at me and makes me laugh
Even when I'm sad
Remembering funny stories
Oh my gosh he's such a dad.

The Mountain

Euan Crawford, Age 10
Haig School

Shooting down the mountain
Over the ice and snow
Where were me and dad going?
Frankly we did not know
CRASH
Where did that barrier come from?
I was tumbling and sliding
But luckily for me
My dad was the saviour
He was there to grab me
I still remember what would have happened
If my hero hadn't caught me

My Special Grandad

Isabelle Masters, Age 9
William Wordsworth School

Knee knocker
Door locker

Funny man
He always can

Game winner
Puzzle spinner

He is my Grandad
He is the best

He is better
Than all the rest.

The Hero of my Life: My Mum!

Oneileia Bryan, Age 12
Windsor School

The hero, the one who I can trust
The hero, the one who makes me feel safe.
The hero of my life is my mum.

My mum is the one who missed half
Of my life. But when I fell
She found a way to pick me up again

When my heart was broken
She found a way to mend it again
The hero of my life is my mum

If I cried she would wipe away my tears
It's like seeing my life slip away
The hero of my life is my mum.

My Grandpa is my Hero

Macey MacDonald, Age 5
Haig School

Grandpa is nearly bald
He is middle sized
He reads me a bedtime story
He lets me watch TV

Grandpa makes me smile
He's got big smelly feet
He makes me feel better when I fall
With a cold pack and a plaster

My Mum is my Hero

Seren Lloyd, Age 5
Haig School

When I fall over my mum helps me
She makes me laugh
She cooks my tea

She takes me to the park
She reads stories
To my brother and me

The Game

Morgen Bowerbank, Age 9
The Haig School

All of the family play a game
After poor old Dad walks
In from a tired day
Well my Mum cooks the tea
You can smell the potatoes boil,
But, my dad looks at me
And my sister too
If I do not win I sulk
That's why my dad loves me.

My Dad is a Hero

Lewis Clay, Age 6
Haig School

My dad is tall
My dad is strong
My dad helps me
We play games all day long

My dad is happy
My dad is funny
My dad is nice to me
So is my mummy

My Great-Grandma the Land Girl!

Paige Hughes, Age 13
Gloucester School

My Great-Grandma Anne is my heroine. Although she hasn't gone through war on the front line; she has witnessed what went on in Britain whilst all the brave men went and fought. She may have been a young lady, and thought of as weak and defenceless, but she still had fire in her belly.

At 16 years old, in 1939, she was conscripted into the Land Army. She was now a Land-girl. The Land-girls were women who took over the jobs of the men who had gone to fight in World War 2. She served in Lincolnshire, as a rat-catcher. As a rat-catcher she would be called into factories and houses to catch the rats that came off of the streets.

In 1943, she met the love of her life, my Great-Grandpa Jack. At this time he was a miner. He met my Great-grandma at a Tea-dance in a village near Wakefield where they both had lived, but had only seen each other in passing. They went out on a few dates and then realised they were each other's forever. Now she is 87 and has a family of her own.

Two years ago she was awarded a medal and Prime-Ministerial letter, in recognition of her services through out World War 2. Although some people may say that women are the weaker sex, without the Land-girls our country wouldn't be like it is today.

That is why my Great-grandma is my heroine.

Our Other Heroes

Anyone can be a hero!

Rob Swinhoe, Age 14
Gloucester School

A hero is a doctor...a surgeon...a hobo or a teacher...

A hero saves lives and teaches the lessons of life,

A hero is a shop keeper...your mum and your dad...

A hero prevents crime and makes peace

A hero is a police Sgt...and army officer...and even your mate...

A hero is brave...courageous...thoughtful and kind,

So if you have what it takes....Step up and be your local hero.

Hero

Robin Davies, Age 12
King's School

Hero? Who could they be?
A friend, a stranger, someone you see?
A selfless act that inspires everyone
The good deeds have only just begun

A bright shining light that glistens down
Tells you never to give up hope
Your role model, rival, whatever they are
They're your bright shining star

Is everyone a hero? I ask you today?
Are we all a warrior in our own little way?
I guess we are, it's within each of us
One day it'll come whilst sitting on a bus

My Hero

Joshua Daly, Lucy McCulloch &
Curtis Menary, Ages 8,7,7
Robert Browning School

Heroic, intelligent
Excellent, achievements
Respectful, caring
Outstanding, brave
Super, magnificent

Heroes

Archie Austin, Age 9
Slim School

Heroes are helpful, selfless and brave.
Even doctors are heroes and save lives
Rescue teams rush to disasters to help others
Off goes the policeman, to answer the call for help
Every day, fireman fight ferocious fires
Some heroes are ordinary people.

Hero

Katie Mallion, Age 14
Windsor School

Tossed like a rag doll on a seething sea,
The orphaned vessel struggles amongst rabid waves
Ever close, look treacherous shadows
These jagged rocks spell danger
Unbeknowing and unwitting, a tragedy beckons.

A light sea mist is now sinister fog
The night's inky blackness compounded
But piercing through depressing gloom, a rhythm
A recurring light, pulsates protection, salvation,
A lighthouse rises firm and proud.

A red and white trident, alerts sea-faring folk
The lighthouse conductor, alone and adrift
Has weight on his shoulders and life in his hands
'souwester'd and caged courageous and selfless
Thoughts only for others in their time of need.

Hero Hero

Chloe Herd, Age 10
Ayios Nikolaos School

A hero is a tall, dark, shadowy figure
A hero is brave, loving and kind
A hero thinks of others before
Themselves

A hero smells the sweet smell of success
A hero tastes the taste of honour
A hero feels the strength of courage
A hero can be anybody from a teacher to a soldier

A hero will save anybody who needs it
A hero can be young or old
If a hero is a hero once, will be a hero forever

The Majestic Hero

Niraj Gautam, Age 10
Hornbill School

My hero is brave like a man dashing through bloodthirsty sharks
As strong as a giant tornado
Like a bizarre black hole in the depths of the universe
Loyal and courageous

A gallant leader
Fierce like a mad bear
Always majestic
Thinks of others before himself
Full of empathy

My hero is like a golden sun in the Earth's core
Willing to sacrifice his life for others
Has fun on every mission like there is no tomorrow
It's all in a days work for my majestic hero.

Heroes

Kate Chapman, Age 6
Ayios Nikolaos School

A hero is someone
He saves people
A hero is someone
Who cares for other people
A hero is someone
Who loves people
A hero is kind
A hero is helpful
A hero is fantastic
A hero is wonderful

Hero

Charlotte McMullan, Age 15
Windsor School

Can you define a hero?
A name, a word, a phrase, a statement
Can they be singled out?
Or are they all around us?
Do we see them every day?

Is your hero the same as mine?
Are they brave and courageous?
Or do they just present themselves that way?
Are you a hero or am I?
Do you know a hero?

I do

We are all heroes.
Whether we believe it or not
We may not present ourselves as one
But our actions speak for us

When you help someone out
When you offer generosity and human kindness
When you save someone's life
When you save a country's life
Or even when you smile at a stranger

Fact is everyone is a hero
Even if we are not labelled one
Soldiers, Nurses, Doctors, Charity workers
Are they not all heroes?
Well so are bin men, factory workers, business men,
Care workers; just look around you.

The list is endless
And ever-growing

My Hero

Lauryn Dunn, Age 10
Dhekelia School

You'll always be there for me
You are like a fearless lion
As bold as a champion
Helping me to break free
Never refused
Soft as a petal
Hard as rock
You will never leave me behind
You have helped me all through my life
I trust you.

My Hero

Momo Jordan, Age 11

Gloucester School

The day I was born I saw him holding me. We grew together like best friends. We could never be apart for a day. When we were together it was like the sun shone. Sadly, he passed away but I stood strong. Now I carry a memory of him to keep me strong. My Hero.

Hero

Isabelle Robinson, Age 13

Windsor School

A hero can be anyone at all
It doesn't even matter who you are
You don't have to be big, strong or tall
You don't need money or a nice car
Stand up for beliefs and do what is right
Don't worry about what people think
Be a good person and you'll see the light
Fears will go and worries will shrink
Heroes don't have to fight or be violent
They can do very different things
They could speak or they could be silent
Or maybe a hero is someone who sings
Listen to your heart and don't be afraid
And inside of you a hero is made.

My Hero & Heroine

Lanieta Vukiduadua, Age 8
Bishopspark School

For a little love...
I would pick flowers with thorns without any
  protection
For a little love...
I would battle an animal with sharp horns
For a little love...
I would work hard to get some money to buy new
  sparkly stuff
For a little love...
I would go to a faraway place and bring some fruit
  back
For a little love...
I would go to an enchanted forest to bring wild
  flowers for you!
For a little love...
I would go to an enchanted forest to bring wild
  flowers for my hero and heroine!

Heroes

Nicole Musson, Age 12
Gloucester School

A hero is a person who helps his friends and neighbours.
Who thinks of himself last and his team mates before.
Some fight for the rights of others, some lend a helping hand.
Some help the community, some fight in a foreign land.
Whether soldier, doctor, nurse or fireman,
All make a difference no matter where you are.
Man or woman, no matter who you are.
Heroes come in different shapes and sizes.
So just open your eyes.

My Hero

Newson Rai, Age 10
Hornbill School

My hero is as bright as a light
Gallant and humble
Quicker than a flash of lightning
Nothing can stand in his way

My hero stands tall and majestic
Like him the Himalayas as hovering over the world
A legend, a saviour of all
He's like dynamite blasted up into the sky
Loyal and brave heart of life

Hero

Nicole Cook, Age 14
Windsor School

I see a hero in everyone
As I walk through the busy school hall
The hero that's hiding in the young
And the ones that have answered their call
I see a hero in my mum and dad
They have always loved me with all their heart
They always smile even when they are sad
I know nothing can tear us apart
I see a hero in my best friend
She is so strong willed and bright and free
Even as we are left facing the end
She is still standing here right beside me
When we learn to get back up after we fall
The hero inside will shine from us all!

Everyone's a Hero

Eleanor McClafferty, Age 14
Gloucester School

I was a hero yesterday
Helped an old lady in the street
She'd fallen and hurt both her wrists
So I helped her onto her feet

My friend was a hero today
She donated some blood to a girl
She didn't even know
And in return she got a Twirl

My brother was a hero today
He saved my dog from my little sis!
She was hugging him to death
And trying to give him a kiss

A fireman was a hero today
He ran into a burning building
And brought out two young children
Who for their mum they were yearning

My school was a hero last week
They raised money for help for heroes
Simply by doing a sponsored walk
Which raised more than a hundred Euro!

So you see everyone's a hero
You don't have to have powers and capes
Just courage and determination
Heroes take every shape.

My Hero

Amelia Loader, Age 8
Robert Browning School

Helpful and caring
Especially kind
Respectful and always
Achieving things
Overcoming lots of fears
Excellent and clever
Super brainy and brave

My Hero is.....

Lucy Horsford, Age 13
Windsor School

My hero is funny, thoughtful and kind
Whenever I think of them
Happiness fills my heart and mind

My hero is strong, courageous and wise
Their strengths kept hidden deep inside but
When trouble approaches
They rise up and shine

My hero is caring and considers everyone's views,
They fight for the weakest
Even if they might lose

My hero inspires me and helps me
To believe in myself
And gives me the strength
To get up off the shelf

My hero is selfless, brave and dignified
Whenever I think of them
I am filled with pride.

Who is a Hero?

Jessica Balchin, Age 13
King's School

Since they were little, kids have been told
About flying heroes who never get old
Superman may be good at fighting cartoon crime
But horrible things have happened in realistic time
Slavery and abuse came and stayed
And no superhero came to their aid
Until a few had the courage to get up
And help all those people who were stuck
Martin Luther-King risked his life to free blacks
And after he did it he was shot in the back
Everyone was grateful for his act of bravery
Now he is people's hero and his speeches are savoury
Mother Theresa was a kind old lady
And she spent most of her life, saving people and
babies
No matter what the illness was she always helped
them
And she is still in people's hearts when an attack
strikes again
Most people have a hero but others do not
They can be real or from a cartoon shop
I don't have one but I admire many people
And one day I could help create a hero.

The 4–legged Hero

Petra Hlavata, Age 12
Shape International School (British Section)

My hand was sweating as I tightly held the dark leash. It was rubbing and burning against my hand as Diego pulled me through the big stones. I tripped over a large rock – as it half covered the floor. I pulled a bit on the leash to stop the dog pulling. Diego was a beginner, all wild and excited, which wasn't so good. But, he did an excellent police dog. I didn't agree about *me* having to bring a dog to Haiti – I didn't work very well with them. Diego was like all the police dogs, a German Shepherd, but to me he was some sort of different. Special.

I looked around, shocked. All the houses that were once proudly standing up, were now lying lifeless on the ground. I couldn't believe my eyes. Rescuers were all around, searching, digging. Suddenly, Diego did a little whine. I stared deeply into his dark eyes. I could see that he was tempted to do something. I didn't know what. He began running and pulling me towards a large pile of mud and bricks. There were no rescuers around, so I didn't understand why he wanted to go there so much. I pulled him towards the rescuers to see if we could help with anything. But he was wriggling and pulling so hard, that he somehow managed to unleash himself. He sprinted like lightning towards the large pile and began digging. I ran after him, quite getting what he was saying. I began removing large stones and called the rescuers. They came over and eventually pulled out a little boy. He was smiling – he must have been happy to be alive – rescued.

Well, it turned out that Diego was the Hero, and I was the proud partner. From then on, Diego's name became Hero.

Surgeon

Stewart Bristol, Age 9
St Andrew's School

Once when I was 2
One surgeon saved my life
By fixing my head
Because one metal swing
Hit me because I was not careful
Hurt a lot

Maybe I Could Be....

Hannah Strong, Age 14
Gloucester School

Maybe I could be Superman
But I'm sort of scared of heights.
Or maybe I could be spiderman
But I think the outfit's a wee bit tight.

Wolverine, Batman, the Incredible Hulk
I think too many people would stare.
I haven't the height or even the bulk
Plus radiation's bad for your hair.

Maybe I could be elastic Reed
And take care of the other three
I'd try my hardest to do a good deed
But I can barely take care of me.

Wonder woman, Cat woman
Let's just give that a thought
With all those skimpy outfits
I'll end up going to court.

Captain America or Cyclops
Optical energy inside my eyes
I could be fighting WW2,
And donning my cape and off to the skies.

If I was a superhero
I wonder who I'd be
There's so many to choose from
But I know there's a hero inside of me

My Hero

Phoebe Trotter, Age 10
Dhekelia School

From the valiant Jupiter so
To the noble earth I know
The element of fire
Drink your time away
You saved me
I could dream my life away

My Hero Poem

Bethany Benson, Age 10
John Buchan School

Mother Theresa

My hero was Mother Theresa because she did not think about herself always about others.

My hero was Mother Theresa because she cared about other people not just herself.

My hero was Mother Theresa because she looked after others when they are sad.

My hero was Mother Theresa because she always was there for them who are alone and not with families or friends.

My Hero

Abigail Sargeant, Age 9
Ayios Nikolaos School

My hero is Craig Bushe
You can find him at Zion Gardens Zoo

He is known as the Lion Man
Eager to learn about all big cats
Raising lion and tiger cubs to trust him
Only Craig has their trust

Heroes

Esme Howard, Age 14
Windsor School

Nelson Rolihlahla Mandela swallowed hard as he looked at the hard walls of his prison cell. He smiled to himself, twenty-seven years in prison altogether, this would be the last morning of many. Nine days ago, anti-apartheid restrictions had been lifted and now, he was almost free. His cell door opened and he looked anxiously down at the paper that lay folded in his hands. He walked down a corridor of murderers, thieves and gangs of wild people and rightfully still saw his anti-apartheid actions as a good thing, not something to be imprisoned for.

Nelson could barely see the outside world for long, before he was put straight in another car and taken to the radio station. As he walked through the long corridors towards the main room he got the usual mix of adoring smiles, grins and viscous scowls. It was good to be back in the world once again. A smiling woman shook his hand with a grin on her face and with a short greeting and a cheerful congratulations, he was on the radio.

Here is an actual part of what Nelson Mandela said on the radio on the 11th February 1990:

"Our resort to the armed struggle in 1960 with the formation of the military wing of the ANC was a purely defensive action against the violence of apartheid. The factors which necessitated the armed struggle still exist today. We have no option but to continue. We express the hope that a climate conducive to a negotiated settlement would be created soon, so that there may no longer be the need for the armed struggle."

I think that this is what makes a true hero, if they are willing to stick to what they believe and fight for it for an unlimited time.

Neil Armstrong

Patrick King, Age 9
Andrew Humphrey School

He helped his fellow crewmates,
In his struggle to the moon.
He was very courageous
I am inspired to be a space man
He made a famous speech
He represents his country
He made it to the moon
So that's why he's my hero
"One small step for man
One giant leap for mankind"

Teacher for the Day

Jenna Kew, Age 7
Episkopi School

Mr Kerr is ill in bed today
So I said I'd be the headmaster
And look after things. He told me it
Was really hard but I said it was dead
Easy,
So...
I was late for school
I called Mrs Barber, Mrs Pepper pot
Gave the children cakes at snack-time
Gave the children a sticker for nothing
Let them go to sleep in assembly
I didn't do the paperwork
Let them play monopoly during numeracy
They can wear bikinis and swimming costumes
Let them play on the apparatus during history
If they want they can use felt tip for their work
Put lemonade in their water fountains
Let them learn what they like and can wear
Jewellery and high heels at school

It took me all day
But I don't have everything finished
And I was really tired
But I am glad Mr Kerr
Isn't ill everyday

And you know what ...
So is Mrs Barber

My Hero

Michael Wojokic, Age 11
Dhekelia School

My hero is the planet Saturn
He is the centre of my horizon
He is as cute as a kitten
He is the best of the light
He is always on time
He is the sweetness of lemonade
And the shock of electricity
He is a romantic sunset setting over the crystal blue waters of the ocean

Nils Bohlin is my Hero

Charlie Lawley, Age 8
Blankenhagen School

Dear Nils Bohlin,

You are my hero because you changed the world.
Many people will not know who you are or what you have done. Your designs have saved millions of people all over the world!
If I could meet you, I would say 'thank you' for inventing the seatbelt. You have inspired me to become an inventor just like you when I am older. I want to invent something that makes a difference in the world!

My Hero

Victoria Copsey, Age 9
Bishopspark School

My hero is delicate
As a feather pleasantly hovering around
This makes me feel extremely inspired.

My hero is tall
As a happily growing giraffe.
This makes me feel mildly miniature.

My hero is beautiful.
As a brightly coloured new born butterfly.
This makes me feel admiration.

My hero is talented.
As a supreme super star.
This makes me feel admiration.

My hero is Darcey Bussell.

Jade Goody

Rhianna Tomlinson & Lusiana Serevi, Age 12
Gloucester School

Joyful
Achiever
Dedicated
Energizing

Giving
On top of the world
Original
Determined
Young

My Hero

Ella Annan, Age 11
Dhekelia School

My hero is from Mars
He is a big soft sofa that can envelop you in a cuddle
He is a fearsome tiger
He shines in the dark like a burning sun
He is a hard wooden solid table that never scratches
He awakes me from bad dreams
He is effervescent, cold lemonade which makes your
mouth dazzle and pop
He is my best friend, making me laugh with joy
He is always my favourite film
He is intrepid, brave and unafraid to fight the bad guys.

Mr Wright the Best Teacher Ever!!!

Bethany Bourne, Age 9
Andrew Humphrey School

Mr Wright is my teacher,
He saved a little boy and a grown man,
He helps others with their work,
He is special to me because he is my teacher,
And he never yells.

He asks politely when making a request,
He respects who we are and helps us,
He never leaves us alone when hurt,
Hes tall and thin and very funny,
And very smart (especially when it comes to maths)

Lionel Messi

Layla Payne, Age 9
William Wordsworth School

Skilful winger
Crowd bringer
Speedy scorer
Trophy storer
Best player
Team stayer
Dead ball king
Injury sting
Goal sighter
Argentinian fighter

My Hero

Kayleigh Chapman, Age 8
Bishopspark School

My hero is graceful.
As graceful as a beautiful, delicate, ballerina dancing softly on air.
This makes me feel incredibly inspired.

My hero is elegant.
As elegant as a snow white swan gliding through crystal waters.
This make me feel delightful.

My hero is a super star.
As super as a shooting star flying through space.
This makes me feel light hearted.
My hero is Leona Lewis.

My Heroine

Juniah Louisy, Age 9
Bishopspark School

I know someone
Who is a very fast runner,
I know someone
Who works extremely hard,
I know someone
Who has the most special smile,
I know someone
Who has very long legs,
I know someone
Who is a gold medallist champion in the Olympics,
I know someone
Who is very honest,
I know someone
That I would ask for an autograph....
If I was ever lucky enough to meet her.

Do you know Kelly Holmes?
She is my heroine.

My Hero

Grace Allcock, Rupak Tamang &
Alicia Cinnion, Age 6
Robert Browning School

I am an author of lots of books
I am a funny man
You will find my books in the kids section
The people in my book are not really alive
Who am I?

I am Roald Dahl

My Hero

Charlie Tippett, Aidan Tinnion, Abbie Thompson &
Jason Headington, Ages 6,7,6,7
Robert Browning School

I wear lots of shiny crowns
I have many pretty jewels
When you are 100 I send you a letter
I have blue eyes
I am the boss of the Army
Who am I?

I am Queen Elizabeth II

My Hero

Kieren Gerry, Bethany Seymour &
Mitchal Avery, Ages 6,7,7
Robert Browning School

I save other people when they are in trouble
I shoot webs at other people who like to be nasty
I jump onto other buildings
I am in a film
I am in a book
Who am I?

I am Spiderman

My Hero

Lillie Herrington, Keiton Robinson &
Dylan Aanes, Ages 6,6,7
Robert Browning School

I write books
I write books in a café
I am a good author
I am not shy
I am clever at story books
I was born to do it
Who am I?

I am JK Rowling

My Hero

Rosie Griffiths, Chanel Fisher &
Nathan Sowerby, Ages 7,6,7
Robert Browning School

I looked after poorly children
I never thought of myself
I tried to look after them very well
I raised a lot of money
I went to church
Who am I?

I am Mother Theresa

My Hero

Andrew Byrne, Oliver Megson, Joe Laverick, William Smithurst, Ages 7,6,7,6
Robert Browning School

I am very fit
I am very rich
I am very good at scoring goals
My fans think I am super cool
I am married to a spice
I play for England
Who am I?

I am David Beckham

My Hero

Alex Rudd, Daniel Federick &
Meadow Pym, Ages 6,7,7
Robert Browning School

I am hardworking because I want to win
I am always sweating
I am as strong as possible
I am healthy and cool
Who am I?

I am Johnny Wilkinson

My Hero

Ryan Kelsall, Elizabeth Knowles &
Kirsty Pye, Ages 8,7,7
Robert Browning School

They are a bit cool
They are never apart
They are quite funny
And they look friendly if you see them
Who are they?

They are Ant and Dec

The Quest for the Red Dragon Egg

Kira Sprake, Age 9
Slim School

In a magical land where dragons lived there were two gleaming suns and two dull moons, in a cave in the kingdom or Krokan were two very special eggs.....They were dragon eggs one was red and the other blue. One day the evil queen Evelyn for the Kingdom of Evingard came and stole the red egg. Two children were playing near the cave their names were Jon and Wendy. After the Queen had left the kids decided to enter the cave and have a closer look. When Jon banged his head on a sharp rock and cried out.!!.SSSHHH!!!! said Wendy the Queen might come back and hear you. Then Wendy tripped over the blue egg. What is this said Wendy...It's a dragon egg replied her brother. Hurry!!!! Lets hide the egg at home before the Queen comes and takes this one as well. When their mother Lucy caught them trying to hide the egg in their room. She asked: What are you doing with that??? The children explained what they had seen and together they decided to visit Mr Tid who once was a rider in the Dragon Legion. The egg started to hatch just as they arrived.
Mr Tid took one look and said it's a water dragon: What's your name he asked. Silvermist replied the Dragon, but where is my sister? Jon and Wendy explained about the stolen egg. We have to save her before she is a month old and take her to the Island

of Fire and Mist or she will become an outcast. I know of a shortcut to Evingrad. It takes us through the Troll Mountain Caves which are guarded by a grumpy old Troll called Warty Walter. When they arrived at the caves Warty Walter bellowed who dares to disturb me if you can answer my riddle I will let you pass unharmed!! The riddle went: what is born of an egg and the colour decided what it is going to be? A Dragon the kids shouted at once! Warty Walter was very cross but let them pass! His final warning was beware where you go the path is hidden unless you know how to reveal it! They walked on and soon it got very dark Lucy started to sing a song to encourage the kids. There was a glowing light showing them the right way. Welcome to Evingrad said Mr Tid as they stepped out of the caves. On a nearby mountain they saw a huge fortress. My sister is being held in there I can feel it said Silvermist! The children and Lucy decided to go and see if they could find out where the Dragon was being held while Mr Tid and Silvermist stayed hidden. When they got to the gates the nasty Guard Captain called blackheart stopped them and asked them questions. The kids managed to keep their secrets, but found out that the Dragon was in the East Tower. The returned to Silvermist and Mr Tid where they hatched a plan. Jon, Wendy and Lucy returned to the Fortress and told Captain Blackheart that they knew where another dragon was hidden. So they walked back to the forest but

Blackheart got suspicious and dragged them in chains back to the castle. Meanwhile Mr Tid and Silvermist were able to free the red dragon named Firestorm who once released from her magical chains grew to match her sister. As they flew to escape Silvermist sensed that the kids were in trouble and came to their rescue.....she landed in the Courtyard and began to fight with Captain Blackheart who was soon joined by Queen Evelyn.

The kids watched in amazement when Firestorm came to help her sister and their combined power turned the Queen and her evil helper to stone. This story proves that you don't need to be an adult to become a hero. Just the courage of two kids and the love of siblings can overcome all.

About Grosvenor House Publishing Ltd. and The Little Books

Grosvenor House Publishing was originally set up by two authors, Kim Cross and Jason Kosbab who had become frustrated with the traditional mainstream publishing system.

The Little Book initiative was created whereby GHP would try and help every schoolchild in the country who loved writing, become a published author in their own right.

The hundreds of schools that have participated in the Little Books project have been amazed at the enthusiasm that their pupils have demonstrated in creative writing when they're told that their stories or poems will be published in a real book. All of a sudden the classrooms are full of would-be writers with ideas and stories abounding.

Why not have your child write their own stories or poems and have them published in their schools very own Little Book and see how enthusiastic they get about writing? For more information, please visit our website **www.thelittlebooks.co.uk** or phone 01483 243450.

www.thelittlebooks.co.uk

School Testimonials

Chappel Primary School
"Just wanted to thank you and the company for the Little Book of Stories & Poems you produced for us. They looked fantastic (note use of past tense - they've all gone!) and the children and their parents thought they were wonderful. We are hoping to make the book an annual event - showcasing some of the children's best work. We are a small village school, and with no history of publishing our children's work, this was seen as a real 'first'. Expect to hear from us next year! Once again, our thanks to all concerned - not least for the extremely fast turn-around time. Full marks!" Richard

Palace Fields School
"YIPPEE! Our books arrived today and they are fantastic! Our new headteacher is so pleased that he telephoned our local bookshop and local press so that we can promote our children's work to everyone on the island. Thank you so much." Helen

Oxley Primary School
"The books were received today. I would like to thank you for your excellent service and quality books. The children are really proud of their achievement and I hope to organise more book projects in the future!" Jeanette

Dallow Primary School
"We are all in love with the books which arrived yesterday. Everyone has commented on how wonderful the books are. Many expecting them to be 'poor quality books, done on the cheap' were particularly surprised at just how good/professional the books are. Our Local Educational Authority has requested a copy of our book in order to help them sell the idea of publishing with your company to many other schools within their jurisdiction.

Thanks so much for all the work that has gone into producing the books and the extremely quick turnaround. Everything has been better than we had expected." Mathew

Author Endorsements

"The Little Books is an excellent way of harnessing the creative energy of young minds. Not only do the children have the fun of writing, they actually see the published result, get feedback and please the parents – not to mention the school piggy bank."

- Fay Weldon

"These Little Book of Stories are a wonderful way to inspire our young students to get excited about writing. Having original stories and poems published motivates children and gives them a real sense of accomplishment. As a writer, I know how much it means to see your work in print, and how exciting it is to be able to share a book with your family and friends. I hope these very special books will give children across the UK lots of encouragement to keep creating and sharing their thoughts, dreams and stories".

- Katharine Holabird

"All of the contributors should be supported and the parents, aunts, uncles, grandparents and family friends who purchase this book will not only help in the necessary funding for the school but will also provide a vital ingredient that your child desperately needs........... encouragement".

- G.P. Taylor